ADA
the Ayrshire

**The cow everybody loves
(in someone else's herd)**

Published by Countryside Press
a Division of Farm Journal, Inc.
Washington Square,
Philadelphia, Pennsylvania

Library of Congress
catalog card number 77-118875

Cow By The Tail

"Ada the Ayrshire must be the most famous cow in the world. Tell us about the man who draws those cartoons. Some of them are priceless and all are wonderful. The cartoonist has to be a dairyman."

So wrote a FARM JOURNAL reader in 1962, echoing hundreds of letters Ada has inspired over the years.

The fact is that Walt Wetterberg, who created Ada in 1941 and portrayed her until 1968, is not a dairy farmer. Not any kind of farmer at all.

He was born and raised on a farm, but as he says: "I surely didn't see anything funny about cows then."

It wasn't until much later on a visit to a friend's farm that he began to appreciate cows. "They are about the only creatures around these days that can take things in stride," says Walt.

Wetterberg's lack of cow experience is only a little less than his lack of formal art training. "I took five hours of art courses at the University of Montana, but I had to quit college when I ran out of money. I doubt if I would ever have become a cartoonist if it hadn't been for the Depression."

After college Wetterberg took a part time job with a department store mostly making window displays. The rest of the time he devoted to drawing, hoping to work into full time cartooning.

Not long after that came World War II. At about the same time Wetterberg received his draft notice, a letter arrived from Arnold Nicholson at *Country Gentleman,* the magazine in those days at the pinnacle of its eminence in agricultural journalism. Could Wetterberg create a believable cow character and a series of cartoons about her? Indeed he could.

"I don't recall now why I decided on an Ayrshire. Probably because I admired the breed's distinguished looking horns," says Walt. "First I was going to call her Arlene, but my girl friend had a sister by that name and I was afraid of offending her. So I settled on Ada and sent off ten cartoons before I went into the Army. As a result, I got scads of letters all through the war from women named Ada. One threatened to punch me in the nose if she ever caught up with me."

Wetterberg drew a few more cartoons during 1942, sending them to *Country Gentleman* from such un-cowlike places as Fort Leonard Wood and Hawaii. Then Ada was put out to pasture while he did a three-year stint of active duty overseas.

"Out of the army in 1945, I had almost forgotten about the cow. I took a little vacation and then decided to submit some more ideas about her. The series started running then until 1948, was dropped for awhile and resurrected again in 1950. When *Country Gentleman* merged with FARM JOURNAL in 1955 I thought that was the end of Ada. But Carroll Streeter, the editor, asked me to continue the series 'for awhile.'

"My main problem with Ada was to keep coming up with new antics that were believable. After I did the first ten in 1941, I felt that I had completely exhausted the subject of cows—there are after all, only so many things a cow can do. And every time I sat down to draw another Ada, this problem loomed like a stone wall at the end of a one-way alley. I guess I must have drawn nearly 675 Ada cartoons over the years and every time I reached the same conclusion: There is not now, nor will there ever be, any more that a cartoonist with a skimpy knowledge of cattle can do with a cow. How would you like to be wrong 675 times?"

Wetterberg rarely got his ideas from other people. "Most situations readers suggested in letters weren't usable or at least I didn't think so. Still, something someone else would say might give me an idea indirectly. I used to sit down with a clip board and a stack of farm magazines to get me in the right frame of mind. Then I'd start doodling. I guess that's about the extent of my creative process. Hardly exciting, is it? I think my earlier drawings were horrible. But after the war, people would laugh at anything. They needed to laugh.

"Maybe we need to laugh more today. Life seems to have become so grim, even farming. Yet, as I noticed in the army, sometimes the saltiest humor arises in the most desperate of times. For humor—good humor—has a way of getting closer to the truth than facts. Where you find no humor, you find people afraid of truth.

"One thing I know for sure. Cartoons do not actually *make* people laugh. Appreciation of humor depends upon a person's own experiences."

Finally the day came when Wetterberg's "one-way alley" really did have a stone wall at the end of it. "If you ask me to draw one more cow," he wrote in 1967, "I'll be tempted to jump off Sugarloaf Cliff at Winona. I've already been up there eight times, but the rocks below look so forbidding."

While Walt had milked Ada dry, success had come his way in other areas, demanding more of his time. His cartoons on other subjects had appeared in just about any magazine you can name, and now he had a chance every cartoonist dreams of: a syndicated comic strip.

So FARM JOURNAL turned wily old Ada over to the capable hands of Jim Zilverberg, another cartoonist of long standing, and Ada has continued to bedevil and charm FARM JOURNAL readers.

Hundreds of cows have been named after Ada, and those of us who have worked with dairy cattle —no matter what breed—know there are legions more whose personalities warrant the name. We've collected the best of Wetterberg's cartoons here and added a few stories about other cows who must be Ada's direct descendants—even though some of them are Holsteins.

Have a good laugh. Farming may not be a bowl of cherries, but it's not a wailing wall of profits and losses either.

Gene Logsdon
Associate Editor, Farm Journal

Our cows
never talk back

I've always thought only farmers in our neck of the woods talked to animals and things.

Like my father. Without doubt, he's the most garrulous man alive . . . with things that couldn't possibly talk back.

"Go ahead and blow off, you stupid roof," he shouts at the tin-covered barn during storms.

And one of his favorites: "Bless you, bulk tank, you do keep a cold melon."

Naturally, one must eavesdrop to hear such talk. One thing Father cannot abide is being caught in the act of talking to an inanimate object.

On the other hand, our neighbor Geeby Bewaldi (everyone thinks that's a made-up name) carries on conversations with his tractor outfit that can be heard 20 acres away.

"Quit squeaking," he roars at the disk. "I just greased you an hour ago!"

Sometimes his threats dissolve into abject pleading that has the ring of classic poetry.

"Don't run out of gas, now," he begs the tractor. "We've only got two more rounds to go."

Geeby becomes downright gabby when he's fixing something. Like when a burr is rusted to a nut and refuses to budge. "Well stay there then," he yells. "I didn't want you to come off anyhow." Then, to make sure the nut got the message, he whacks it with the wrench.

But I've found out that farmers are carrying on one-way conversations everywhere.

Once I worked for a farmer in Minnesota who loved to sing in the field, but he claimed that every time he did, something broke down. He almost convinced me, too. No more than five minutes after he'd start singing there'd be a loud "caroom!" . . . followed by a big cloud of smoke and dust and a high-pitched burst of profanity.

Willy would stand back and glare at the offending machine. "Dammit, can't stand to hear me singing, can you? Just can't stand to see a man happy." He'd keep talking like that all the while he repaired the break. Willy was stubborn, but after a while you wouldn't hear much music out of him. I guess he came to an agreement with the machine. If it would work, he'd quit singing.

As I approached the barn of an Indiana friend, I overheard the following: "At least you could co-operate here in the barn . . . all you did all day was lay in the shade."

There was no one in the barn with my friend. Not a hired man, not a boy, no one. Yep, you guessed it. He'd been lecturing a cow.

Come to think of it, talking to creatures and inanimate objects may not be as safe as it used to be. *You have to be pretty careful what you say to a computer these days!*

Gene Logsdon

I tried to solve the great milk pricing mystery

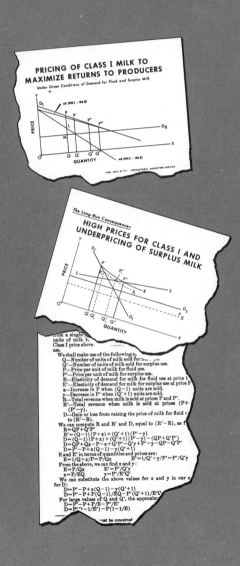

One day after I'd been milking cows for five years, I looked at a milk check and realized I didn't understand why I was paid $4.250376 a hundred for my milk.

"Well, you got two kinds of milk," dairymen would say. "Class I and Class II. They blend these, and come up with a price somewhere in between."

When I'd asked who set the prices BEFORE the blending, fingers pointed wrathfully toward Washington.

I'd go to co-op meetings and hear officers discussing formula prices and everyone nodding like it was all plain as day. When I'd ask why, they all drifted away. Finally an assistant administrator helped me.

"You start out with the basic formula price for manufacturing milk the preceding month," he began condescendingly. "You divide the total Class I use of Grade A milk by total Grade A producer milk to get the current supply-demand ratio."

"Where does that preceding month's price come from?" I'd repeat patiently.

"Once you get your supply/demand ratio, subtract that from the computed daily—"

"Just tell me where the original price comes from and I'll quit bothering—"

"Then you add the current supply demand ratio for this month, then subtract the standard . . ."

"WHY?" I thundered.

He looked at me curiously, "Tell you what. I'll have the USDA send you background literature."

For three days the mailman bombarded me with pamphlets and books containing theoretical discussions of milk pricing—geometric designs, graphs, and words like "maximize" that weren't even in the dictionary. (See tables at left.)

A retail milk company official I questioned snorted. "The government figures it out on a slide rule after they audit our books. Audit, audit. We're just a glorified public utility!!"

The Depression started it all, said the executive director of one state milk commission. Things were so bad farmers wanted to call in the government. If nothing else, it was nice to have someone to blame. And most of them still feel that way.

I agreed to that. I'd be in favor of Federal milk pricing, I think, if only I understood it.

The executive continued: "We base our milk price on (a) the cost of production; (b) the amount of Class I milk sold out of total sales; (c) a price in line with other products; and (d) the average price for Midwest manufacturing milk."

"Well, if your price is based on cost of production, why hasn't milk gone up in the last 20 years?"

"Sometimes one consideration cancels out another."

Now I was getting riled. I managed to corner three milk-pricing experts where they couldn't get away.

"You've shown me by using basic formula prices, cost indexes, pool receipts, average daily sales, consumer income indexes, supply/demand adjustment factors"—I gasped for breath—"how you arrive at a specific price. But you begin with a manufacturing milk price from the preceding month, which in turn comes from the month before that. WHO SET THAT PRICE? Adam? The First Continental Congress?"

"Well, we get that from auditing pool receipts. That's what the handlers paid for it. It's sort of supply and demand."

"Well, not quite," said another, toying with a slide rule. "Remember the government maintains price supports on butter and skim milk."

"And it depends on the type of pool in effect."

"Individual pools are more competitive."

"Marketwide pools make a fairer price."

But I quit listening. I'd found a copy of the new Cotton Bill, and was wondering if anyone could explain that!

Gene Logsdon

Ground Hog Day

1

2

3

4

1

3

5

2

4

6

Horrors...
a parlor full of adas

the charger

the door pounder

the guard

the lingerer

the outlaw

Whatever your opinion of dairying may be, there probably isn't a word in the English language so ill-suited as "parlor" to describe the room where you milk. My dictionary defines parlor as a room primarily for conversation, relaxation or the reception of guests. Need I say more?

I well remember our optimism when we put together our first milking parlor. We had reams of blueprints giving dimensions for a variety of designs. Booklets told us how to do everything from mixing cement to cleaning glass pipelines.

But as for getting the cow into the parlor, this was shrugged off as merely a matter of training.

I will not go into all the lurid details of the first time we tried to run our herd through the milking parlor—how a three-inch pipe imbedded in concrete and bolted to a beam above was torn loose from its moorings; how one cow even managed to ram her head through a fluorescent light in the ceiling; what can only be humorously referred to as a holding pen was twice battered down by the charge of the Holstein brigade; how the exit door—two thicknesses of hardwood—was torn from its hinges and splintered against the wall.

We developed a different definition of parlor. The "conversation" was exceedingly one-sided and scarcely of parlor variety. The "relaxation" was enjoyed only by those cows that we pushed bodily into the parlor. And the "reception" of visitors would have driven Amy Vanderbilt to cigars.

Out of that ordeal, I have formulated the following data which you will need if you intend to operate a milking parlor.

1. When building, beware of specifications made for cows. Think in terms of Sherman tanks.

2. On occasion expect to find as many as three cows in a place where only one is supposed to fit.

3. If you find your parlor suddenly occupied by four cows more than its capacity, *get out quick.*

4. Consider beforehand the limits of your bravery and strength of heart. Until you stand in a

milking pit and see a stall gate swing toward you with a cow draped over it, you do not know fear.

5. While working in the pit, wear a space helmet.

However, if you live through it, your cows will come to accept the parlor as a way of life. After that, your herd will develop a more or less set pattern for entering the parlor. In this pattern you will distinguish the following cow types:

Chargers. These cows come into the parlor without any trouble at all. They fear neither man nor beast in their desire for grain and they may trample you if you get in the way.

Door Pounders. Door Pounders are Chargers who don't get into the parlor with the first batch. They keep butting the door to let you know they didn't. Door Pounders develop into Door Openers unless you have rigged a system that would stump Houdini, in which case they may turn into Door Knocker Downers.

Guards. Such cows will not come into the parlor of their own volition. But they will stand mulishly in the open door and butt away other more timid cows who do want to come in.

Lingerers. Lingerers can take it or leave it alone. If you have an hour to spare, they may finally make up their minds to saunter in.

Outlaws. In nearly every herd there will be a few cows who never come into the parlor unless forced. An excellent way to cull cows without keeping records is to get rid of all outlaws.

For those of us who think a milking parlor is still the best way to get the job done, I suggest this sort of information be furnished when a cow is sold to a dairyman:

She should be typed according to parlor manners. Chargers of two or three years standing should bring premium prices. A known Lingerer should sell below par in the parlor milking market. An outlaw should be placed in a category just a shade higher than canners and cutters.

Gene Logsdon

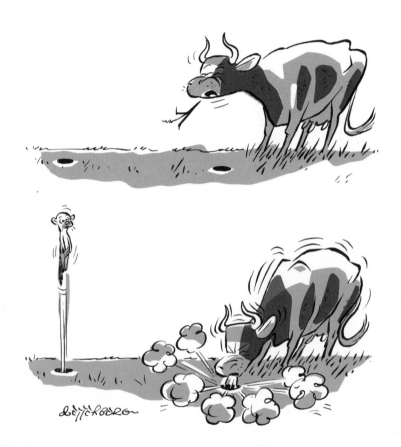

"Hey Ed, here's what's wrong
with our head count."

Why do I keep this darn cow?

"Oh, I know, I know!
You've had a hard day in the loafing shed."

She's an "udder dunker." Picks the lone mud-hole in the pasture for her siesta. That's Hyacinth, our family cow.

And on summer mornings when I have corn to cultivate and hay to rake, where is she? In the farthest corner of the pasture, a quarter of a mile of dew away. She has a hollow leg for grain, and I'll swear she can inhale a bale of hay.

Why, then, keep her?

Well, partly because she gives us all the milk we can drink, cream for coffee and strawberries, sour cream for cake and biscuits—even for butter. (We don't churn any, but it sure gives you a sense of security to know you could.) My milk-bottle neighbors josh me about her, but I think they envy my foaming pails of the real article. Bad weather can shut off their milk, but mine is always on tap.

That morning walk to the far corner of the pasture? Oh, there's nothing like a walk through the dew to wash the sleep from a man's eyes and the dust from his shoes. And those days when she's nowhere to be found, and I follow hoof-prints through the garden—I wonder then if she wouldn't make better hamburger than milk. But as soon as I see her frolicking with the neighbor's heifers, I realize she needs companionship; the life of a family cow is a lonely one.

Milking's no nuisance. I've only to rattle a feed pail, and out of the winter darkness comes the gentle creaking of hoofs: old Hyacinth, sleep-eyed and blinking. The milk starts to sing in the bucket. Later, when the milk foams in the pail, that's the time for contemplation, for organizing the day— and in evening, for looking back. These moments of solitude a cowless farmer never knows.

I guess I have to admit I love our old cow. Perhaps that's the answer: To be completely happy with a family cow you must be an animal lover, not an economist.

Rex R. Gogerty

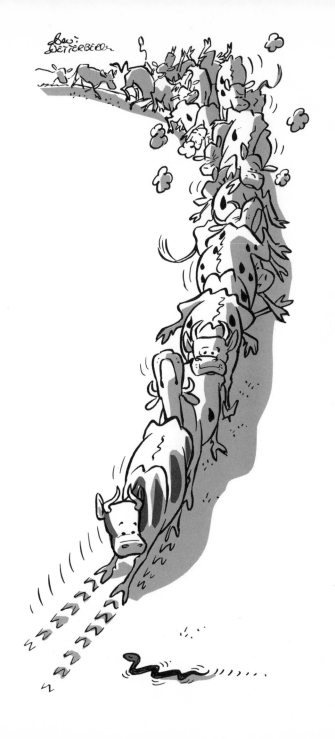

Why men took over milking

There's only one thing lower than a grave robber, and that's a man who would stoop to milk a cow. So stated the medieval farmer to his wife— trying his best to duck the job.

Even today, milking cows is not every farmer's cup of cream. "In parlors?" asks Bud Sees, staring out across his Dakota cattle ranch. "I wouldn't milk 'em, if they were in the Waldorf Astoria."

For countless ages, men saw to it that milking was woman's work (along with most of the other homely chores necessary for survival). That left men free to go to town and run for public office.

But naturally men still wanted to boss the job. "The worst point of housewifery," said a Mr. Markham in 1660, "is to leave a cow half milkt." Francis Guenon in 1867 was even more unctuous. Milking "seems better fitted to females who are likely to be more gentle and clean." But in case they weren't, he had plenty of advice for them:

"Go to the cow stall at 7 o'clock . . . dowse the udder well with cold water . . . keep your hands and arms clean. Milk each cow dry, as you suppose, then begin again with the cow you first milked and drip them each . . . Suffer no one to milk a cow but yourself (can't you hear the men cheering) and have no gossiping in the stall . . ."

No wonder women took to wearing bloomers and marching for equal rights!

But likely as not, milkmaids would have gone on quietly milking the cows were it not for machines. The first patent for a milking machine was granted in 1859. It was a simple piston pump that removed air from a sealed pail and sucked the milk up—like the plunger on a beer keg in reverse.

Women bent dutifully but with sighs of relief to pumping and the men stood around with hands in pockets grinning at the machine and winking at the girls. There is no record of what the cow did, but I bet that you and I know.

One day that piston pump broke, and the milk-maid, being a woman, couldn't fix it. So the man rushed to her aid (wanting to keep her bent to the task or else *he* might have to do it) and from then on, man, the tinkerer, was hooked. The term dairy-MAN came into existence.

But it was a difficult transition. C. S. Plumb admitted in 1900 that "men dislike to milk cows and so numerous machines have been invented by them. Most of these are foolish contrivances and none are real successes . . . Men will continue to devise however, and it is probable that at some time large herds will be milked by machine."

Back in 1895 when Tonganoxie was just a Kansas Indian, Modestus Cushman invented the first pulsator. But really practical milkers didn't appear till after the turn of the century, when William Lawrence and Robert Kennedy of Scotland developed a mechanism for controlling pulsations. The first U. S. patent on a double chambered teat cup was granted in 1903.

As long as women were tending the cows, milking three times a day was considered necessary. But when men tinkered their way into the dairy, they abruptly decided that twice a day was enough. And nearly every generation of dairymen breed a few who try to milk only once a day.

With men at the helm, other milking conditions have improved too. Cows come to the milker instead of vice versa, and they stand on raised platforms because men have weaker backs than women. Pipelines rid the man of the job of carrying milk, and heated parlors keep him from freezing to death, as he does not have that extra layer of female fat under his skin.

And what about these gentle, cleanly females whose very natures fitted them especially for milking cows? They are going to town and running for public office.

Virginia B. Shriver

1

2

3

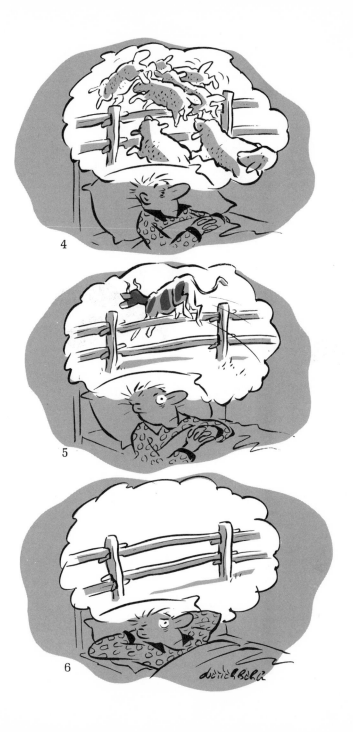

"Never mind the precipitation probability."

3

4

Bum steer

Any mother of a boy showing a calf at the County Fair will recognize Clyde and Charley

"That," said my friend Eleanor, waving her hand at a fold of 125 sheep, "is a 4-H project that got out of hand!" Ah yes, I thought, but at least that flock took a few years. Clyde and Charley were out of hand almost from the beginning!

Clyde and Charley were Hereford calves acquired by our 14-year-old Dane when the 4-H steer club drew lots. Husband Paul and I admired their square brown bodies and their curly heads as we bedded them down in the old horse barn, little suspecting the adventures we were heir to.

When a sobbing boy burst into our bedroom before dawn the next morning crying, "Dad, my steers are gone!" 4-H took on new meaning: Hurry, Hunt, Help—and a brief expletive muttered by Dad.

Out we all went in boots and pajamas. It was our first chase and the most memorable, but not the last. "Charley slipped his halter!" became a rallying cry that brought everyone to his station like a volunteer fireman. The neighbors chased, the mailman chased, the school bus driver chased and on the day we hosted the church picnic, everybody including the preacher chased.

Clyde and Charley grew in bulk, despite the exercise, while we Leimbachs developed the lean look of trackmen.

Like most teen-agers with wheels in their heads, Dane had happy visions of the Honda he would buy with cattle profits. Two steers bought for $270, gently tended and nicely fattened, might bring $600 at a successful fair auction—a profit of $165 each. Wow! First feed bill brought the dawn of truth.

"Gee, Mom, it's gonna cost me $300 just for feed, and I've got hay to pay for besides that!" It became evident that in a year, two steers could easily eat a Honda. Charley got a runny nose, and a vet bill was subtracted from diminishing profits. In the feeding and grooming process five buckets were destroyed (cost $4.25). Dane needed two rope halters (rope, $2) and a TB test (veterinarian, $7). He faced a fiscal fiasco.

The grooming of a 4-H steer for show is a process that makes men out of boys and heroes out of fathers. In those weeks before the County Fair, a steer must be trained to walk docilely around a show ring, whisking his combed tail flirtatiously, stopping at the tug of a halter, lifting his head and setting his feet to show his deep brisket and his broad rump to advantage, and otherwise impressing the judges that he is a prime beast.

Charley was obliging as Dane trimmed his hooves and curried his rump. He displayed his conformation as though it were his glory and not his doom. Clyde had other ideas about grooming and it fell to Dad to teach him better ways. How thrilling for a wife to watch a steer dash up the lane towing her true love by the seat of his Bermuda shorts. Watching her spouse turn a couple of somersaults and arise bruised, bleeding, but still in command of the animal and his halter, confirms in middle age her early conviction that he is of heroic caliber.

Three times in one evening an angry Paul dragged a mutinous animal back to the training ring with brute force. The word *bullheaded* suddenly became graphic. ("Gee, Dad," I muttered, "where were you when I was trying to train the kids?")

When Fair week finally came, a wary investor lay down in the Junior Fair barn beside his four-legged investment. Would Dane lead Clyde, or would Clyde lead him? Would the sale price cover expenses or was the whole year's work and worry gone for nought?

Grandma and our suburban relatives came by to wish Dane well. "Beautiful animals," they said, but what did they know? Truly Charley was beautiful, but Clyde was obviously built for speed. One wisecracker suggested that if he didn't make it in the steer class, we might put him in the trotting races. Cattlemen walking by would remark, "There's a lot of daylight under that animal." His back sagged and no amount of currying would conceal his ribs.

On show day Charley, scrubbed and combed, was set aside as one of the top three contenders in the ring. One promising animal was being shown expertly by a shapely girl with flowing blonde hair. While Charley's trainer stood transfixed by the blonde, Charley relaxed like a matron let out of her girdle, and was dropped to fifth place. Dad tried frantically to signal Dane.

Clyde was on his good behavior; he ran Dane briefly about the ring, but fell in line just as Dad prepared to vault the fence and take charge. But soon Clyde was relegated to the lower end of the line with others who "also ran."

The auction was a success. The comely blonde trainer of the Grand Champion inspirited the buyers as well as the 4-H boys. Charley as No. 5 animal brought a price that balanced Clyde's slimmer pickin's. But even then the total only covered Dane's feed debt. When the steer check came in the mail, he handed it over glumly, "Here you are, Dad. I guess it's all yours for the feed and hay."

He had known that there would be no profit, but this was surrender and it hurt.

"Well, Dane, you learned what we all learn sooner or later, that investments don't always pay a dividend. The margin in the cattle market can be like Clyde—thin. I've fed a lot of cattle and some years I've given away my hay and corn. What Clyde and Charley ate won't make me a poor man, so you just give me what you paid for the calves and we'll call it square."

Dane's face brightened; he was relieved and delighted, but he wasn't about to blow his cool.

"Gee, Dad, you're all heart!"

"Yup," said Dad, "I'm 4-H clear through—Heart, Head, Health, and Hand-in-the-pocketbook!"

Patricia P. Leimbach

1

2

1

3

2

4

Cure a kicking cow?

The return-backlash widow maker is nearly always lethal.

With back legs tied, she became a wild, pounding pile-driver.

SHOOT HER!

Our award for the best understatement of the decade goes to *The New York Times* which strayed from more familiar paths some time ago to discuss kicking cows. "The milker can prevent the upward movement of a cow's leg," quoted the *Times* studiously, "by pushing his head into her flank, *but unless he is wary she may outwit him.*" (Italics mine.)

Verily, verily, friend. Unless he is wary indeed. Allow me to tell you about this creature, the kicking cow *(bovinus destructio)*. She has outwitted whole nations of the wariest of all wary people, namely farmers. Unlike humming bird wings, ricocheting bullets and rock slides on the moon, the cow's leg in the act of kicking has never been photographed because no one knows when it's coming. When it does, it is already past.

In general, you can distinguish at least three generic types of kicks: 1). The Single Hop-Kick used to result in one foot in the bucket but now just means one set of milking cups ground into the cement. 2). The double Hop-Kick. That put two hooves in the bucket formerly; now it requires ordering a new milking unit. 3). The Side Delivery Widow Maker. It comes in three versions, all capable of laying Cassius Clay out cold. The return-backlash variation of this kick is nearly always lethal. It starts as a high Side Delivery, catching you in head or shoulder on the way forward before it reaches the cow's front flank. Then the hoof comes stabbing back in an arc just about a foot lower than its forward motion, disintegrating everything in its path.

Fortunately for dairymen, few *bovinus destructio* develop the return backlash. But old No. 73 did. In fact, she had perfected every conceivable kick in the books including the Horse Smash which is hooves straight back, catching the unwary traveler passing in the rear.

Against this monster we threw the collected genius of farm tradition. Hobbles, ropes, flank pincers, chains, soft music, extra feed, everything. Nothing availed. Any contrivance that bound both her back legs together merely turned her into one horrible up-and-down pile driver, grinding inflations and teat cups to pieces. Seeking to circumvent this, I tied a rope to one of her legs, fastened the rope to a block and tackle lashed to a barn pillar behind her, then drew the leg completely off the ground, so that she stood helpless on the other leg. As I put on the milkers, she sagged over and fell on me.

We had little trouble getting old 73 in the stall of our new parlor that first time. Penned in a cage with only about 6″ leeway on either side and above, she seemed harmless enough, but I lashed her back legs to the steel pillar behind her anyway, and with a smirk, hung on the milkers. About that time, she finished wolfing down her feed and let out a low, nerve-shattering moan. She lunged forward, backward, sideways, then all three directions at the same time. The spanking new parlor began to quiver at its very foundation and I panicked. If I did not cut her loose, she might pull the whole blooming building down on me. As I moved in close, sawing the rope frantically with my dull pocket-knife, she went down on her belly, twisted grotesquely, and hit me square on the chin—*with her right front hoof!*

We sold old 73. And now we know the only wary thing a man can do with a congenitally kicking cow. Treat her the same wary way cattlemen handle cows with foot and mouth disease.

Gene Logsdon

"Next!"

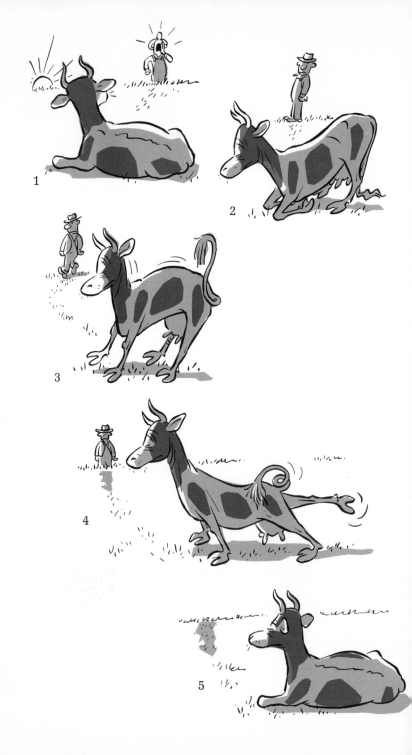

The cows are out!

We should have been more suspicious of the Wisconsin heifers we bought to start our dairy herd. Not that I doubt their pedigree; I just wonder how they got to Ohio. After observing them and their offspring for several years, I've concluded that they made the journey on foot, nostrils flaring, tails flying, and hooves lacing to mincemeat any fence that stood in their way.

To our family, the cry "COWS OUT!" has come to rank with "FIRE!" or "EARTHQUAKE!". Unless you've hunted buffalo on the plains or bargains at a women's clothing sale, you can't imagine the terror of facing our stampeding herd.

Night raids are the most frightful. A mild, wet winter darkness always brings out the worst in our herd. Settled cozily in the house, we suddenly hear that sickening sound of jingling neck chains swinging from a hundred running cows. Like firemen, we leap frantically into boots and rush out into the night. A herd needs to cross a soggy lawn only once to turn it into a hog wallow.

We have learned to react to a break-out with a speed that would have left Paul Revere gaping. On occasion, when someone has spotted a cow going through a fence, we have marshalled two cars, two tractors and a horse into the field before the last of the herd found the break.

Sometimes speed is of no avail. Like the time when we knew we had 100 Holsteins roaming somewhere around our 300 acre farm, yet there was not a cow in sight. They had vanished into the cornfield.

Through the green jungle we chased, following the sound of cornstalks snapping off. On through our fields, through McCarthy's 100 acres into Loverich's 150 acres, the blundering herd rolled. Even with the help of other farmers, fighting to save their farms from the invading herd, it was dark before we got the last cow home.

Age did not bring mellowness to the herd. They simply passed it on to their offspring. Hoping to offset heredity with a new environment, we moved the calves to Grandad's farm just north of town.

One morning soon after, a state patrol car drove up. Visibly shaken, an officer told me the cattle had been out on the highway playing chicken with the Larks and the Falcons. Even now, he said, the calves were being held under surveillance in the parking lot of a drive-in-restaurant up town. I grabbed a bucket of grain. They couldn't hold those calves with tanks, much less surveillance.

We followed the calves' escapades by police radio, as sheriff, constable, city police, and state patrolmen spread the dragnet.

"Six calves at 8th and Bigelow, heading north."

"Impossible. Six just ran through the Farm Bureau elevator. Over."

"Black and white ones? Over."

"Yep. Over."

"They're all black and white," I volunteered from the depths of the back seat. "All twenty of them."

"They're all black and white," my officer barked authoritatively into the radio. "All—" he turned sharply to me—*"Twenty* of them?"

I just nodded. He should have been glad it wasn't a hundred. By now, rounding up the herd has become a sort of community affair. By telephone apprehensive neighbors keep us aware of every sag in the fence, every move the cows make. Boyfriends bringing girls home from late dates often take a swing around the farm to make sure all is well. And you could empty church in 10 seconds simply by whispering loudly:

"Logsdon's cows are out!"

Gene Logsdon

"What do you suppose they
know that we don't?"

"She doesn't just eat. She's really a bottomless pit."

"She's a master of feminine tricks to obtain her share of sympathy."

"You don't actually own a cow; she owns you!"

"She never really sleeps; too busy testing your fences!"

No wonder they call her BOSSY!

For years writers have extolled the dairy cow as a contented, generous "foster mother of mankind," or as a placid, peaceful, but just a bit stupid, animal.

Well, 'tain't so. All of that is pure hokum, and I wouldn't be surprised if the cow *herself* hasn't promoted the whole idea!

Actually, she's a *discontented, self-centered, greedy, excitable, cowardly slave driver.* Those are harsh words, I know. But before I'm jailed as a subversive, let me prove my point.

Heaven only knows, *the cow should be contented.* From the day she's born until she dies, she's pampered. She's taken from her mother by The Man, and is hand-fed a diet fit for a queen. She's allowed to grow into young cowhood with no responsibilities whatever.

And when the time comes to seek a mate, does she have to fight her way through hordes of other clinging females? *She does not.* She rolls her big brown eyes, puts on a few girlish airs, and takes a few skittish gallops. The Man rushes like mad to the telephone to arrange for love and marriage through the local artificial breeder.

She spends a full nine months of leisure, feeling no pain, losing no breakfasts, preparing no layettes, just enjoying herself. When she has her baby, The Man and possibly The Vet, too, are there to see her through.

Meanwhile, The Man has been enjoying no such

leisure. He has been footing her grocery bill with blood, sweat and tears. He has been planting feed for next year, hauling feed from the fields, and doing chambermaid work for her comfort.

She doesn't just eat, she's a bottomless pit. Bales of hay, tons of grain, bushels of ensilage, gallons of water, all properly enriched, must be pitched, shoveled and carefully garnished with molasses.

If The Man doesn't provide for her dainty, sanitary comfort, her pal, The Milk Inspector, sees that he does.

While The Man spends endlessly on machinery to take care of these chores, the cow and The Milk Inspector (neither with a penny invested) stand by with self-satisfied smirks.

The cow is *completely* greedy. She'll go to any length to get her groceries. You'd think with *four stomachs* to keep her going, she'd be happy. Sometimes she finds too much. But unlike other animals, does she leave some for another day? Not her. She loads up all four stomachs to the point of death, just in case there's no food tomorrow.

She'll bawl to *get out* of the barn if she thinks there might be something edible outside. And then she invariably concludes that she's missing something and bawls to *get back in.*

She's author of the "guaranteed wage." Where else could such an idea have originated? She eats 365 days a year, whether she earns it or not, with eight weeks paid vacation.

A buxom thousand-pounder, she's the world's biggest coward. A tiny heel fly can put her to flight. She'll cower at the unexpected sound of a sneeze, and a change of clothing on the part of The Man makes her *nervous.*

Any man who talks about the cows *he owns* is a dreamer; the realist knows how many cows he is *owned by.*

All family activity is planned around the cow. If The Man does get away for a breather, the cow decides how far he can go, when he must come back, and is a constant worry while he's gone.

For sheer pathos, I refer you to the sick cow. She's a master of feminine trickery when it comes to getting sympathy.

She lowers her long silky lashes, rolls her liquid eyes, gets a dejected hump in her spine, and sends everyone into panic.

What does she have? *Heart trouble, cancer, the plague?* No! Just an old-fashioned bellyache, probably from trying to eat more than her share.

Generous? Hah! A cow doesn't *give* milk. It's taken from her forcibly, at great expense and labor.

Placid? No, again. Just plain lazy. All of the textbooks tell you how much water a cow will drink! Sure she will, *if you bring it to her.* But let bad weather come, or if the creek happens to be a long walk away, see how much she'll drink then!

She's a born tyrant, a firm believer in the caste system. Watch any herd and you'll see that there's a boss cow whose authority is *never* questioned. Any new cow in the herd is immediately challenged, and put in her proper place.

I've heard that a cow doesn't really sleep. This doesn't surprise me. She's much too concerned with casing the joint for places to go through fences.

There probably hasn't been a lock invented even yet that'll keep a cow out of where she shouldn't be.

She's far from stupid. She can even tell time, not because of desire to accommodate you by coming into the barn, *mercy forbid,* but because she knows there's feed in there.

And never make the mistake of thinking that they're all alike. On our farm we've had glamor girls, extraverts, introverts, worry warts, motherly types, business women, career girls, screwballs and nervous wrecks. But that would be another, and *even longer,* story.

Instead of trying to tell you *all* I know about cows at one time, I'm going to the refrigerator and get myself a good cold glass of milk.

Lois Rebecca Prout

"Sometimes I wonder what
they see in each other!"

1

2

No blue ribbon for Mom

I wasn't trying to disrupt the livestock sales yard. I simply was trying to help my high school son get a picture of his FFA calves. But the man galloping by me on horseback shouted as if he thought me deaf as well as a little dumb: "Lady, get out of the alley, or you're going to get hurt!"

Another voice bawled over the loud speaker: "Thirteen head! Alley one! Pen eighteen!"

I grabbed my purse, camera, and the Future Farmer's small brother, and started to scram. "You can't leave now!" someone yelled. "They're coming down the alley!"

Just in time, we shinnied up the fence. Thirteen head of wild-eyed steers raced by, their horns fanning my ankles.

We made three other attempts to get out of the way; but each time, a bunch of cattle was hustled toward us, and we had to seek the fence top again. I gave vent to my exasperation by screeching at my 5-year-old: "So help me, if you ever join FFA or 4-H, don't you expect any help from me!"

I didn't mean it, for of course he will join. And so will the Future Farmer's other younger brother. And I shall remain knee-deep in baby chicks, vegetables, fat steers, and bottle-fed lambs—all those many projects necessary to the making of a boy into a man.

Show me the boy who has earned merit badges, medals, blue ribbons, or a trip to a national meet —or, for that matter, a boy who hasn't won anything, but who is ready to try again next year— and usually I can show you a mother who should look like a general with a chest full of ribbons.

But Mom's ribbons and badges are not so tangible. They are the pride she wears (right there on her sleeve) in the accomplishments of her boy; and her own realization that it's as necessary for her to help and encourage that boy, as it is for her to feed him and make him wash behind the ears.

Sometimes I wish I were the woman whose chief concern when Fair time rolls around is to get Grandma's vinegar cruet entered in the antique section. And sometimes I envy the unharassed poise of my city friends who can stroll past the exhibits, assuming that chickens' combs always shine, and that steers' tails are naturally curly.

But I am a little bit sorry for them, too. They've missed the biggest part of the show, known only to those who enter by the back gates armed with buckets and brushes.

I have taken many projects in my stride in the course of our son's 4-H and FFA career. Scouting, too. I have mastered the Morse code, and I have taken the Five-Mile Hike and eaten aromatic stew out of a can. We—Dad and I—have applauded our son's victories, and helped him starch his spine to stand up to defeat. But often I have wished that I had never met Doris.

Perhaps, subconsciously, I feel inferior to Doris because of her pedigree. My ancestry is a conglomeration of nationalities: but Doris's is untainted by any intermingling of blood lines except the best Holstein-Friesian.

She wasn't a very impressive calf the day she made her debut in our family, shivering cold and unable to stand. But as of today, she has a fistful of ribbons—Junior Grand Champion, twice Grand Champion, and Reserve Grand Champion.

Our life has not been simple, nor dull, since Doris entered it. For one thing, the will power of a mule is mild compared with that of a cow if it decides not to climb into a trailer. The only way I want to cope with that situation is to get behind the offender and whop her with a stick.

But Doris must not be struck, nor scolded, nor

yelled at—it would make her nervous. She must be tempted with grain or the best quality hay held temptingly before her. Doris must be coaxed and cajoled, praised and patted, until getting into the trailer becomes her own idea. But once at the fair, she again performed brilliantly.

But as I watched the other youngsters' prize animals being auctioned off, I did not feel a part of the bustle and noise of the sales yard. Men were there, with strident voices, and they belonged. So did the boys and girls scrambling around the enclosures, giving final brushings and pattings to their animals. The white-shirted, cigar-smoking business men in the buyers' section belonged there—but not I. Neverthless I wanted to see this thing through.

Then the bidding began, and I saw a girl weeping into the sleek neck of the steer just sold to the butcher. I saw a boy's face brighten until it glowed incandescently as, quarter by quarter, the price mounted on his pen of fat lambs.

I listened as, again and again, the bidding climbed—Going once, going twice . . . SOLD to the Bank and Trust . . . SOLD to F. W. Woolworth Company . . . SOLD to Barlow Warehouse!

What profit, I wondered, is there in a business man's paying more than the market price for a pig or calf?

The realization flooded over me that herein lies the profit: This is the American way of showing that our young people are our priceless possession. This is our way of saying to them: "It isn't easy to be young, to learn good sportsmanship and good business practices—whether you win or lose. But we believe in you, and we want to help."

And suddenly I was proud to be a part of it. Sometimes it's nerve-racking, fatiguing, and downright inconvenient to be the unsung helper behind the scenes of my son's projects. But it's also tremendously rewarding—a manly son is blue ribbon enough for any Mom!

Eleanor N. Fowler

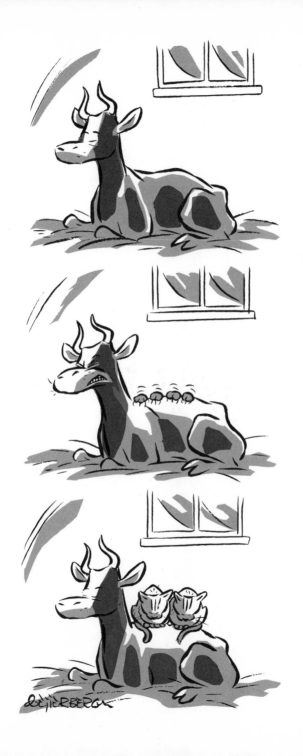

A nightly small adventure

It is the earliest hour on a morning in earliest spring. I crawl from bed at the insistence of the alarm clock. It has been two hours since my husband Bruce came in at 11 p.m. and it's now my turn to check our calving herd.

Close to the living room heater I quietly pull on tights, slacks, rubber boots, sweater, hooded coat, gloves. I step out into the dark, get in the pickup and drive a half-mile to the corrals. As I slip into the feedlot area I shiver a little, wondering what might be ahead of me tonight.

My flashlight picks out a cow, awake, licking salt. Nearby I check each one in the big wire pen.

Now I follow the long fenceline to where the ground falls away a little, close to the river. Here most of the herd beds down. The weather is fine tonight. Sometimes there is a fog that stings my eyes, reflects back the light and makes me feel very alone. Or there may be snow; one night it fell so thick I could hardly find the cows. Rain is worst; once I walked into deep mud and nearly lost my oversized boots. In heavy rain the animals don't bed down. With them wandering around, I am sure to check some several times while missing others entirely.

One of the bulls follows along with me, on the other side of the fence. "Be quiet, Davy Crockett," I say softly, for he's making his peculiar noise—a kind of "meow" that sounds out of place coming from such a great bulk of muscle.

When I reach the main part of the herd I pick a path among the sleeping cows that will not force them to rise. I am looking for any cow that is restless or in an unusual position.

My light shows the friendly, placid face of Sunday, who was reared a pet and always has to say hello. Beyond her are Wrinkle Nose, Fatty and Band-aid. (Most of the cows have names acquired from appearance, behavior or something that has happened to them.)

The whole family cuss and coddle our animals, even lose sleep over them. We are their doctors, midwives, masters, baby-sitters. We fence them in and fence them out. We suffer with them as they are branded, tattooed, ear-notched, blood-tested, vaccinated, inoculated, sprayed. For their protection we ride horses, tractors and fences. In return they get sick, get out, get our goat.

Further on I find a cow licking her just-born calf. I talk to her softly and reassuringly, checking the slippery-wet calf to see if its nose and the inside of its mouth are warm. Mama stays almost touching my head, alternating soft moos with a louder, warning *brrr* sound that would send the faint-of-heart scrambling for safety. (I have been well coached to get myself out of the way if she should become aggressive.)

The calf is doing fine, and in two hours my brother-in-law, our partner, will be along to make sure it isn't chilled. Meanwhile, I continue along the fence, for I've a couple more babies to check. On bad nights the men pick up these youngest calves and house them in the hay barn. When that has happened, the mothers follow me, sure that I possess the magic to return their offspring.

There have been times when I've come upon a bewildered cow whose calf won't answer her urging, for it is dead. If a calf is chilled or a cow is in trouble while calving, I must get help at once. One night we got only four hours of sleep and lost two calves.

But this has been a good night. Back home, I shuck off heavy clothes and slip into a cozy flannel gown, wake my husband enough to report the new arrival, and crawl into bed. I am filled with a warm satisfaction—of being wanted and needed, of having returned from a small adventure . . . and of being terribly sleepy when there is actually time to sleep.

Beth Lincoln Beck

1

2

3

4

2

4